CW00403125

£5.99
UK Only

This book belongs to

Name.. Age......

Address...

....

Galaxy...

ANNUAL CONTENTS

Designed by Simon Connor

Written and Edited By Dan Whitehead for Newsstand Publishing Services

ished in Great Britain in 1998 by World International Limited., Deanway Technology Centre,
Wilmslow Road, Handforth, Cheshire SK9 3FB Printed in Italy. ISBN 0 7498 3758 6

A Long Time Ago...

It began with two droids, R2-D2 and C-3PO, landing on the planet Tatooine in an escape pod. On the run from the evil Empire, R2-D2 was also on a secret mission to deliver important information about the Imperial Death

Star super-weapon to the Rebellion. The droids eventually found their way into the life of a young farm boy, Luke Skywalker. But R2 needed to find an Jedi named Obi-Wan Kenobi before the Empire's stormtroopers found him. Luckily, Obi-Wan found R2 when he saved Luke from an attack by the Sand People.

The Rebellion needed Obi-Wan Kenobi's help. The Death Star plans in R2 were to be delivered to the Rebels on Alderaan. Hiring a cocky smuggler named Han Solo, and his Wookiee copilot, Chewbacca, the Rebels blasted out of Mos Eisley spaceport just as the stormtroopers tracked them down.

Meanwhile, Princess Leia, the Rebel spy who had placed the plans in R2-D2, had been imprisoned by Darth Vader. Held captive on the Death Star, Vader and the Death Star's commander Grand Moff Tarkin demanded to know where the Rebel base was hidden. If Leia refused to tell them, her home planet Alderaan would be destroyed. Leia told them that the Rebels were on Dantooine, but the Death Star destroyed Alderaan anyway. Leia had lied about the base - the Dantooine base had been abandoned long ago.

The *Millennium Falcon*, Han's ship, arrived at Alderaan only to find - nothing!

The entire planet had disappeared and before the Rebels could escape, the *Falcon* was pulled into the Death Star by a tractor beam. After hiding in the *Falcon's* smuggling compartments while stormtroopers searched the ship, the

heroes split up. Han, Luke, and Chewbacca went to free Princess Leia while Obi-wan set off to disable the tractor beam so the *Falcon* could take off again. After a fierce battle, Leia was freed and the Rebels fought their way back to the *Millennium Falcon*. As they arrived at the docking bay, they saw Obi-Wan duelling with Darth Vader. Seeing his friends about to escape, Obi-Wan switched off his lightsaber and let Vader strike him down. Mysteriously, Obi-Wan's body simply disappeared... his spirit had become part of the Force.

With the tractor beam gone, the *Millennium Falcon* blasted off for the Rebel headquarters on Yavin 4. There the Death Star plans were studied, and a weakness was found. If a missile could be fired down a tiny exhaust port, the entire station would explode. The Rebel fleet took off to intercept the Death Star, which was preparing to destroy Yavin 4, and the Rebellion with it. An epic space battle followed, as wave after wave of Rebel fighters tried to get close enough to attack the exhaust port. All were defeated, and Darth Vader himself joined the fight. In the end, it was Luke Skywalker who fired the fatal shot - guided by Obi-Wan Kenobi and the Force - and destroyed the Death Star. Darth Vader spun into space, his TIE fighter out of control.

In spite of the Rebel victory, the Empire was far from finished. The Rebels relocated their base to the icy planet Hoth. Darth Vader had

become obsessed with finding Luke, and sent probes to the furthest reaches of the galaxy. One such probe landed on Hoth, and it was while investigating the crash that Luke was attacked by a wampa. Luke escaped, but found himself exhausted and freezing as night fell. Han rescued him, but not before Luke saw a vision of Obi-Wan Kenobi telling him to go to Dagobah, to learn from the Jedi Master Yoda. But the Empire had other plans. The probe had summoned Imperial forces, and giant AT-AT walkers were advancing on the Rebel base. Luke and the other pilots held off the assault long enough for the Rebel fleet to make yet another last minute escape. Once everyone had been evacuated, Luke set a course for Dagobah.

Han, Chewie and Leia had their getaway in the *Millennium Falcon* but suffered damage along the way. Han decided to stop at Cloud City for repairs. Governed by Lando Calrissian, one of Han's old aquaintances, the group felt sure that a much needed rest awaited them. They were wrong. Darth Vader had hired bounty hunters to find the Rebels, and it was one such bounty

hunter, Boba Fett, who was waiting at Cloud City with Vader. The plan was to use Luke's

friends lives to lure Luke to his capture. Luke sensed his friend's plight while in training with Yoda, the tiny, eccentric Jedi Master who had taught Obi-Wan Kenobi many years before. Even though he was not fully trained in the Force, Luke left Dagobah and went to face Darth Vader.

Vader wanted to freeze Luke in carbonite for transportation to the Emperor, but needed to make sure the process wouldn't kill him. He tested it on Han, much to Leia's and Chewbacca's dismay. Once Vader knew that Han was still alive inside his frozen cocoon, he gave him to Boba Fett, who planned to claim a reward for Han from Jabba the Hutt. This was not part of the deal that Lando had made with Vader, and when told to take Leia and Chewbacce prisoner Lando

turned on the stormtroopers and tried to save Han. Despite his best efforts he was too late. Meanwhile, Luke and Darth Vader battled high above the ventilation shaft of the floating city. Luke was

no match for the Dark Lord. Vader cut off Luke's hand and revealed the shocking truth -

he was Luke's father! Vader implored Luke to join the dark side, but Luke refused and threw himself down the shaft. His fall was broken by a weather vane hanging beneath the city, miles above the planet surface. Luke clung to the weather vane for dear life and soon the *Millennium Falcon*, with Lando at the helm, swooped in to save him.

On Tatooine, Han's frozen body was hanging on the wall of Jabba the Hutt's palace. Working together, the Rebel's formulated a plan to save him. First, R2-D2 and C-3PO arrived at the palace with a message from Luke for Jabba. Luke offered Jabba a gift - the two droids! Then Chewbacca was brought into the palace in chains, captured by a mysterious bounty hunter. That night, the bounty hunter freed Han from his carbonite prison and revealed her true identity - Princess Leia! Han and Leia's reunion was short lived. Jabba captured them both, locked Han up in his dungeon and made Leia his slave.

Finally, Luke entered the palace, dressed in the black cloak of a Jedi. While trying to bargain

with Jabba, Luke fell through a trapdoor operated by Jabba, and found himself face to face with Jabba's pet rancor. Killing the giant creature, Luke angered Jabba who declared that all the Rebels were to be thrown into the mouth of the

terrible Sarlacc. But Luke had a plan, and when R2-D2 fired his lightsaber through the air, the escape was under way. Leia strangled Jabba, and they all fled as Jabba's sail barge exploded.

While the others returned to Rebel headquarters, Luke kept an important promise. He went back to Dagobah to finish his training, but found Yoda on his deathbed. The Jedi Master told Luke that he would have to face Vader one more time to become a true Jedi. Then, Yoda took his last breath and died. Before long Obi-Wan's spirit appeared and explained that Darth Vader was in fact Luke's Father. He had once been a young pilot and Jedi named Anakin Skywalker whom Obi-wan had tried to train. But the young man

had turned to the dark side and become the evil Darth Vader. Luke also had another family member - a twin sister... Princess Leia!

In another part of the galaxy, the Empire was already building a second Death Star, bigger and more powerful than the first. The Rebels needed to strike before this new weapon was completed. An energy shield protected the space station while it was being built, projected from the nearby Forest Moon of Endor. Luke, Han, Leia, Chewbacca, and the droids led a task force to Endor to shut down the shield so the Rebel fleet could attack. There they met the Ewoks, resourceful

furry creatures. Luke told Leia that he was her brother, and then surrendered himself to the Empire in order to face Darth Vader on the new Death Star. Luke believed that Vader still had good in him, but the Emperor revealed that the new Death Star was operational. While Luke watched helplessly, the Death Star fired on the the unprepared Rebel ships. Knowing that the Rebels had walked into a trap, Luke lashed out in anger. The Emperor laughed as Luke and Vader battled.

Soon Luke would turn to the dark side and fall under the Emperor's control. But Luke spared Vader's life, and refused to join the Empire. Furious, the Emperor attacked Luke with bolts of Force lightning. As Luke writhed in pain, moments from death, Darth Vader struggled to his feet and hurled the Emperor into a maintenance shaft to his doom.

Then, as he lay dying, Vader asked Luke to remove his helmet so he could see his son with his own eyes. Luke obeyed him and the two Jedi were reunited. Then Anakin Skywalker died in his son's arms. On Endor, Han, Leia and Chewie were fighting for their lives.

They had been ambushed at the Imperial shield generator, but the Ewoks joined the battle with rocks, logs, and primitive catapults. Despite their blasters and technology, the Empire's troops

were no match for the Ewoks on home ground. Soon the shield generator was destroyed and the Rebel fleet began its attack. Lando led the assault in the *Millennium Falcon*, and sped through the cramped scaffolding and girders of the second Death Star. Even with a squadron of TIE fighters on his tail, he destroyed the reactor core of the space station and blasted back into space. The second Death Star was torn apart, with only a small shuttle escaping the fiery destruction. On board was Luke Skywalker and the body of his father, Anakin. As news of the Emperor's death spread, people and creatures all over the galaxy rejoiced. And on Endor, as the celebrations carried on through the night, Luke looked into the sky and saw a magnificent sight:

Obi-Wan, Yoda, and Anakin Skywalker, all smiling down at him.
At that moment, Luke knew he would never be alone again...

The History Of The Rebellion

It was the rise of Senator Palpatine through the ranks of the Old Republic that first sparked the Rebellion. Fearing the evil and corrupt Palpatine's motives, brave members of the Senate  plotted to keep him from cheating his way into power.

Leading the campaign against Palpatine were Senator Mon Mothma of Chandrila and Senator Bail Organa, head of the Royal Family of Alderaan and adopted father of Leia Organa.
Their secret plot failed and, by various underhanded methods, Palpatine became Senatorial President of the Republic. Almost immediately, he declared himself Emperor and began a reign of terror and military strength. He hunted down and destroyed the Jedi Knights.

The turning point came when the people of Ghorman gathered at the planet's spaceport to protest at the new Empire's cruel tax increases. The Emperor's warships landed on top of the crowds, crushing them. Shocked by such a vicious attack, Mon Mothma and Bail Organa began to divert money and weapons to the various resistance groups that had sprung up to defy the Empire. They also used their positions in the Senate to pass important information to the rebel groups.

At this stage, the Rebellion was nothing more than scattered groups of freedom fighters, with few weapons and resources. In the face of Palpatine's vast power, their efforts were futile. Most of their defences were destroyed, and their home planets placed under Imperial rule. At this point, Mon Mothma's rebel activities were exposed by the Empire's secret police. Bail Organa warned her that she had been discovered and

Mon Mothma fled from the Imperial capital before she could be captured. Moving from star system to star system, Mon Mothma began to  organise the stray rebels into a fighting force capable of taking on the Empire.

During a visit to the Corellian system, she managed to join the main resistance groups together to form the Rebel Alliance. A Declaration of Rebellion was drawn up, and the fight against the Emperor truly began.

More and more worlds joined the Alliance. The Imperial Senate was disbanded, giving Emperor Palpatine complete control of the galaxy. Those members of the Senate who had been helping the Rebels were rooted out and

executed. Only Bail Organa remained undiscovered, and he sent sent a  message to his comrade from the Clone Wars, Obi-Wan Kenobi. Bail Organa's adopted daughter, Leia, played a key role in delivering the message to Obi-Wan, and in getting the plans for the Empire's new weapon, the Death Star, to the Rebels. It was these plans that turned the tide of the war against the Empire, although they came too late to save Alderaan.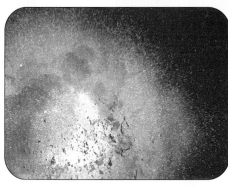

The planet was destroyed as an example of the Death Star's power, ending all life on the planet.

The stolen plans revealed the Death Star's one weakness - that small fighters could penetrate the defences and fire proton torpedoes down an

exhaust shaft directly into the reactor. Luke Skywalker fired the

missiles that signalled the Rebel's first major victory over the Empire.

As the Imperial and Rebel fleets faced each other, Lando Calrissian

flew the *Millennium Falcon* into the structure of the half-built second Death Star and destroyed the core.

The battle station was blown to pieces, taking the Emperor with it. At last, the galaxy was free.

Civil war continued to rage across the galaxy, with the Rebel forces nearly getting wiped out on the ice planet Hoth.

Meanwhile, the Emperor had begun construction of a new, more deadly Death Star. The Rebels had to act... fast.

The Declaration Of Rebellion

You have disbanded the Senate, the voice of the people;

You have instituted a policy of blatant racism and genocide against the non-human peoples of this galaxy;

You have overthrown the chosen rulers of planets, replacing them with Moffs and Governors of your choice;

You have raised taxes without the consent of those taxed;

You have murdered and imprisoned millions without the benefit of trial;

You have unlawfully taken land and property;

You have expanded the military far beyond what is necessary and prudent, for the sole purpose of oppressing your subjects;

We, the Rebel Alliance, do therefore in the name - and by the authority - of the free beings of the galaxy, solemnly publish and declare our intentions:

To fight and oppose you and your forces, by any and all means at our disposal;

To refuse any Imperial law contrary to the rights of free beings;

To bring about your destruction and the destruction of the Galactic Empire;

To make forever free all beings in the galaxy.

To these ends, we pledge our property, our honour and our lives.

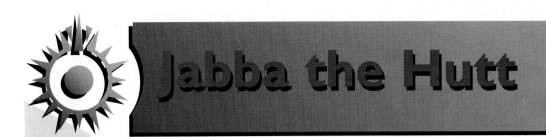

Jabba the Hutt

Not all of the enemies that the Rebellion faces come from within the Empire. Some, like the notorious gangster Jabba the Hutt, operate outside Imperial law. The Hutts are a slug-like race, native to the planet Varl. They have no skeletons and their slimy, wet bodies are formed by massive layers of muscle and fat. Their skin is resistant to nearly all known weapons and chemicals. Hutt arms are of little use, and are usually reserved for shovelling food into their gaping mouths. Hutts have powerful tails that can be used to crawl around, but most prefer the dignity of repulsorlift vehicles to move from place to place. The average lifespan for a Hutt is one thousand years.

Jabba (full name: Jabba Desilijic Tiure) was born into a criminal family. Despite their bulk, Hutts have a natural talent for criminal organisation. After learning from his father, Zorba the Hutt, Jabba sets himself up as a crimelord on the desert planet Tatooine. Full of low lifes, thugs, bounty hunters and assassins, Jabba's palace soon becomes the centre for all underhanded dealings in the sector. Nearly every criminal eventually ends up working for Jabba, including a smuggler named Han Solo. Forced to dump a smuggled cargo of illegal spices, Han finds himself on the wrong end of Jabba's anger and is hunted by nearly every bounty hunter in the Outer Rim. Jabba eventually meets his death when Princess Leia, who was chained in his sail barge as his slave, strangles him with her chains.

Face The Rancor!

Luke has fallen into the rancor pit in Jabba's palace! Can you help him find his way to the exit without getting caught by Jabba's hungry pet?

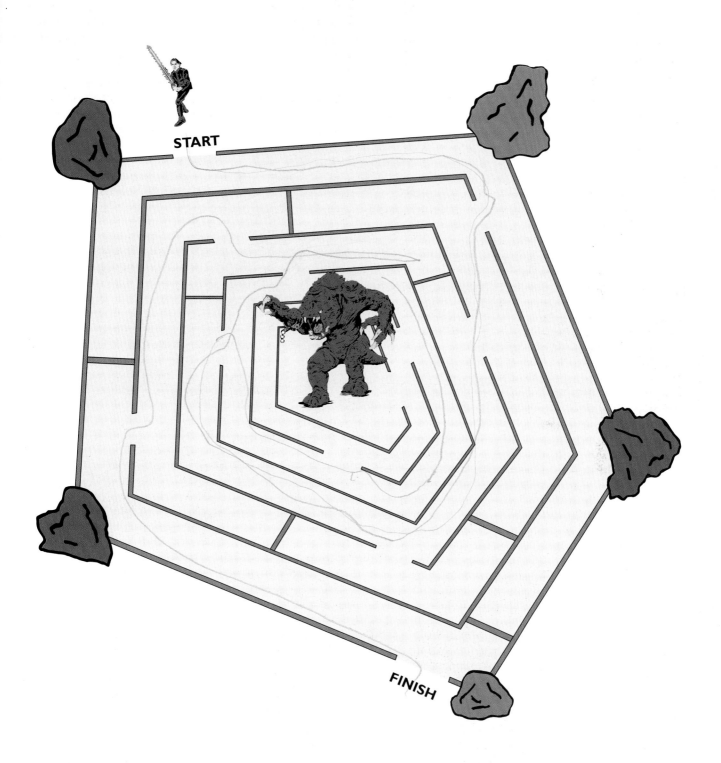

START

FINISH

15

The A - Z Of Star Wars

A is for AT-AT

The terrifying All Terrain Armoured Transport is used by the Empire to transport troops and weapons into battle situations. Despite their heavy armour, a fatal flaw in their design is discovered when AT-ATs attack the Rebel base on Hoth. If the AT-ATs legs are incapacitated, the transport crashes to the ground.

B is for Beggar's Canyon

This valley on Tatooine is where Luke Skywalker practices his piloting skills as a youth. At the controls of his T-16 skyhopper, he hurtles through the narrow canyon hunting womp rats. This proves to be good practice for the Battle of Yavin, in the Death Star trench.

C is for Clone Wars

The Clone Wars took place many years before the rise of the Rebellion, in the days of the Old Republic. Few records survive, but it is known that noble Jedi such as Obi-Wan Kenobi, Bail Organa, and a novice called Anakin Skywalker fought together against the enemies of the Republic.

D is for Deflector Shields

There are two types of deflector shield fitted to spacecraft. One repels solid objects such as asteroids and space debris; the other absorbs energy such as radiation or blaster fire protecting the ships hull from damage.

E is for Ewoks

These curious furry creatures live in the trees of the Forest Moon of Endor. Standing only one metre tall, their ways are primitive, relying on spears and bows rather than blasters. The Empire does not believe the Ewoks are of any importance, but they reveal themselves to be determined fighters who play a vital role in the destruction of the second Death Star.

F is for Force

The mysterious Force is the energy field generated by all living things. Those who are sensitive to the Force can learn to harness its power and manipulate it. . The are two sides to the Force: light and dark. Both are part of the natural order, and without the anger and destruction of the dark side, there could be no light.

G is for Gamorrean

This thuggish, pig-like species is famous for its brute strength and immense size. Adult Gamorreans can stand just under two metres tall, and their thick-set muscles made them ideal for guard duty in Jabba the Hutt's palace. Though Gamorreans can understand most languages, their own speech is restricted to grunts and snorts.

H is for Hibernation Sickness

When a person is revived from a state of suspended animation, hibernation sickness is often experienced. Symptoms include temporary blindness, weakness, aching muscles, and on rare occasions, madness. Han Solo suffers from hibernation sickness when freed from his frozen carbonite state.

I is for Imperial Royal Guard

This elite unit of the Imperial armed forces act as the Emperors personal guards. Only the very best Imperial troops may join the Royal Guard, and they are trained in a wide array of weapons and fighting techniques. They will protect the Emperor with their lives and their loyalty is absolute. Imperial Royal Guards wear crimson robes and body armour.

J is for Jawa

These short, rodent-like creatures are natives of Tatooine and make their living scavenging the desert wastes for scrap metal, rogue droids, and space debris. They then clean and repair the items and sell them to Tatooine's many settlers and traders. Jawas hide their faces in heavy brown cloaks, but their glowing eyes can almost always be seen.

K is for Kessel

This bleak planet is home to the Empire's correctional facilities. Fierce defenses keep prisoners in and intruders out. Those held here are forced to work in local mines, digging for profitable spices. Smuggling of Kessel spice is a dangerous occupation, but Han Solo boasted of completing the famous "Kessel Run" in less than twelve parsecs.

L is for Lightspeed

The massive distances of space can only be covered by travelling through hyperspace, a dimension where normal laws of time and space do not apply. Hyperspace can only be reached by travelling faster than light, and any ship needing to travel through deep space needs a hyperdrive.

M is for Moisture Farms

Luke Skywalker grows up on his Uncle Owen's moisture farm in the deserts of Tatooine. On many arid, dry planets, the harvesting of moisture from the air is the only way to scrape a living from the harsh landscape. Using vaporators to extract water from the air, the farmer can then sell this liquid to travellers or use it to grow his own crops.

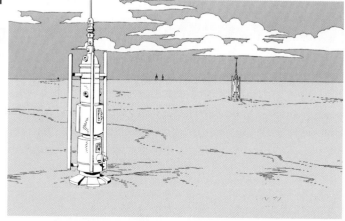

N is for New Republic

After the defeat of the Empire at the battle of Endor, the Rebel Alliance set up this democratic government to sweep away the years of harm brought by the Empire. Its aim is to restore the ideals and principles of the Old Republic.

O is for Outer Rim

The Outer Rim Territories is the name given to the star systems located on the furthest reaches of Imperial space. The distant nature of these systems from the core worlds meant that the Empire conducted some of its most terrible crimes here, hidden from view. The planets in the Outer Rim were pillaged for slaves and resources for many years, so it's no surprise that a large proportion of the Rebellion's support came from these areas.

P is for Probot

Probots, or probe droids, are used by the Empire to gather information about various locations. Using a sophisticated array of military and scientific equipment, the probe droid relays everything it finds back to it's masters. They can return to orbiting spacecraft, but are programmed to self destruct to avoid capture. The Empire uses a probot to track down the Rebels on Hoth.

Q is for Quarrel

Chewbacca's bowcaster weapon fires projectiles of energy called quarrels, which explode when they hit their target.

R is for Restraining Bolt

When fitted to a droid, a restraining bolt prevents the droid from straying and forces them to respond to commands from a handheld device. Restraining bolts are used by Jawas to keep large numbers of droids under control until they can be sold. R2-D2 tricks Luke Skywalker into removing his restraining bolt by promising to show Luke the complete hologram message from Princess Leia, but R2 really plans to escape shortly thereafter.

S is for Sith

There exists a mysterious and powerful group known as the Sith. Little is known about who they are or what their purpose is. Darth Vader was known as a Dark Lord of the Sith.

T is for Tibanna Gas

This gas is extremely rare, but can be extracted from the atmosphere of the planet Bespin. Lando Calrissian was Baron Administrator of Cloud City, a hovering processing factory for the gas. The gas can be sealed in carbonite and shipped off planet to be used in weapons manufacturing.

U is for Ugnaught

The squat, ugly workers of Bespin's Cloud City are Ugnaughts. They work at processing the Tibanna gas, and at other tasks. Chewbacca had to rescue C-3PO from eager Ugnaughts when he discovered the droid, in pieces, heading for a furnace after Threepio has a close encounter with an Imperial Stormtrooper.

V is for Voice Manipulation

One of the most common Jedi powers is the ability to affect another person's thoughts and actions by verbal commands. Obi-Wan Kenobi uses voice manipulation to slip past stormtroopers in Mos Eisley, and Luke Skywalker later uses the same technique to gain entry to Jabba the Hutt's palace. Voice manipulation only works on the weak willed.

W is for Wedge Antilles

One of the Rebellion's best pilots, Wedge flies against the Empire many times, including the battles against both Death Stars. He is a Corellian, like Han Solo, and becomes one of Luke Skywalker's closest friends.

X is for X-wing

The most enduring of the Rebel fighters, the Incom Corporation T-65 X-wing is a small but powerful spacecraft ideal for attack or defence. Luke Skywalker's chosen ship, it is capable of lightspeed and has a socket for an R2 unit, which can interface with the computer to oversee navigation and repairs. The X-wing fighter leads the attack on the first Death Star and remains a key element of the Rebel's military power.

Y is for Yoda

This wizened Jedi Master is the teacher of both Obi-Wan Kenobi and Luke Skywalker. When the Empire crushes the Old Republic, Yoda waits in hiding on the swamp planet Dagobah until Luke Skywalker to follows his destiny to Yoda's doorstep. Nobody knows what species Yoda belongs to, or whether there are any of his kind left.

Z is for Zuckuss

With his fly-like features, this bounty hunter is one of Jabba the Hutt's entourage hired by Darth Vader to locate the *Millennium Falcon* after the battle of Hoth. Unfortunately for Zuckuss, it is the mysterious Boba Fett who claims the price on Han Solo's head.

How Much Do You Know About Luke Skywalker?

How well do you know the hero of the Rebel Alliance? Answer these questions to find out!

1. Luke Skywalker grows up on which planet?
Alderaan
Tatooine
Hoth

2. What do Luke Skywalker's aunt and uncle do for a living?
They repair droids
They are Jedi Knights
They run a moisture farm

3. Which creature attacks Luke on Hoth?
Wampa
Jawas
Ugnaughts

4. Who is Luke's father?
Obi-Wan Kenobi
Han Solo
Darth Vader

5. How does Luke destroy the first Death Star?
He crashes a Star Destroyer into it
He fired torpedoes into an exhaust port
He switches it off at the main control room

6. What does Luke disguise himself as to rescue Princess Leia?
A stormtrooper
Darth Vader
A Wookiee

7. Darth Vader chops off one of Luke's hands. Which one?
Left
Right
Neither - it was his foot

8. How many times do Darth Vader and Luke battle with lightsabers?
Once
Twice
Never

9. How does Luke escape from the second Death Star?

In a stolen shuttle
He uses the Force
In the *Millennium Falcon*

10. Who trains Luke to be a Jedi?

Yoda
Princess Leia
The Emperor

11. How does Luke kill Jabba the Hutt's rancor?

He shoots it
He uses his lightsaber
He crushes it under a giant door

12. What are the names of Luke's aunt and uncle?

Uncle Bulgaria and Aunt Sally
Uncle Owen and Aunt Beru
Uncle Bob and Aunt Ada

13. What happens to Luke in the Mos Eisley Cantina?

He nearly gets into a fight
He wins a game of holochess
He buys some crisps

14. How do Luke and Leia chase the Imperial scouts on Endor?

On skateboards
On speederbikes
By swinging on ropes

15. What colour is Luke's first lightsaber?

Red
Green
Blue

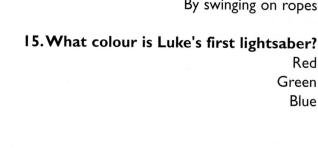

Planet File: Dagobah

This swampy planet resides in a charted, but rarely travelled, star system. Shrouded in mist and completely lacking in spaceports or technology of any kind, it's no wonder almost all travellers give it a wide berth.

Only those who deliberately seek the planet, including the Jedi Master Yoda, bother to land here (and even then they can have trouble taking off again thanks to the boggy ground and heavy foliage). Yoda chooses this as his retreat when the Empire hunts down the Jedi, and he remains here until his death prior to the fall of Imperial Rule.

The sparse population of the neighbouring planets consider Dagobah to be a haunted world, and stories are told of Dark Jedi who terrorised the sector many years before.

Use The Force

Yoda is training Luke in the ways of the Force. Luke must concentrate on the rocks to make them levitate. But that's not all! He must also rearrange them so the letters spell out the names of his friends. Can you help him?

L O H S N O A

H A C E A W C B C

A S E P I L C S E N I R

N O K I B N E B E

23

How Much Do You Know About The Droids?

Did you pay attention to C-3PO and R2-D2's adventures? Let's hope so, or you won't be able to answer these tricky questions!

1. How many languages can C-3PO speak?
Ten
Ten Thousand
Six Million

2. What does Princess Leia hide inside R2-D2?
The plans for the Death Star
The Royal Jewels Of Alderaan
Her sandwiches

3. What does R2-D2 do on Jabba the Hutt's sail barge?
Show hologram movies
Serve drinks
Sweep up

4. What does C-3PO do in Jabba's palace?
Translates
Dances
Serves as a bodyguard

5. What happens to C-3PO in Cloud City?
He joins Darth Vader
He gets blasted to pieces
He finds his long lost brother

6. On which planet do the droids land in their escape pod?
Tatooine
Dantooine
Dagobah

7. Who captures the droids and sells them to Luke's Uncle Owen?
Sand People
Stormtroopers
Jawas

8. What happens to R2-D2 on Dagobah?
He becomes the first droid Jedi
He battles Darth Vader
He falls in the swamp

9. How does R2-D2 free himself and his friends from the Ewoks' trap?

He uses a miniature saw to cut the net
He uses rockets in his legs to fly them out of danger
He impersonates an Ewok

10. How does R2-D2 help Luke, Han and Chewie escape from Jabba's clutches?

He rolls at high speed into Jabba's belly
He creates a hologram of a krayt dragon to scare everyone away
He tosses a lightsaber for Luke to catch

11. Which droid is damaged in the attack on the first Death Star?

C-3PO
R2-D2
C-3PO and R2-D2

12. What does C-3PO call Luke Skywalker?

Mr. Skywalker
Sir Luke
Master Luke

13. R2-D2 and C-3PO are almost seperated when they are sold by the Jawas. What happens?

Luke doesn't like the look of C-3PO and sends him back
Luke's uncle buys an R5 robot instead of R2-D2, but it blows it's motivator
R2-D2 tries to escape and falls down a cliff

14. What was Han Solo's nickname for C-3PO?

Golden Rod
Sparky
Cool Dude

15. When Luke, Ben and the droids visit the Mos Eisley Cantina, what happens to the droids?

They join a wrestling team
They have to wait outside
They get drunk on motor oil

Planet File Tatooine

Tatooine is the primary planet of the Tatooine system. Located deep in the Outer Rim, it is very much a frontier planet, populated by brave settlers, bounty hunters and smugglers hiding from Imperial persecution.

The twin suns, Tatoo I and Tatoo II, beat down on the planet, mercilessly baking the desert ground. Water is scarce, so most settlers rely on moisture farms and vaporators to supply the precious liquid.

Despite its inhospitable terrain, Tatooine is home to a wide variety of species including Jawas, Sand People, banthas, and krayt dragons - not to mention the hoardes of people who inhabit the dangerous townships like Mos Eisley Spaceport.

Luke Skywalker is born and raised here, Obi-Wan Kenobi settles here to keep watch over young Luke, and Jabba the Hutt forges his criminal empire from his palace at the edge of the Dune Sea. For such an out-of-the-way planet, Tatooine has plenty going on!

The Secrets of Tatooine

The shifting sands of Tatooine hide many secrets from the eyes of the Empire. See if you can find the following words in the wordsquare. Words can be up, down, or diagonal.

T	B	F	H	B	A	N	T	H	A
U	D	J	J	M	T	O	R	B	N
S	A	R	L	A	C	C	B	X	I
K	C	W	U	R	W	A	Y	Z	T
E	S	A	D	A	J	A	V	Y	N
N	E	B	O	I	G	M	P	S	A
G	K	X	K	D	A	I	N	U	C
E	M	O	S	E	I	S	L	E	Y
D	A	E	H	R	O	H	C	N	A
A	F	L	Q	P	R	W	Q	H	C

JAWA   MOS EISLEY
TUSKEN   CANTINA
RAIDER   JABBA
BANTHA   ANCHORHEAD
SARLACC

27

Darth Vader

With his black armour and terrifying mask, Darth Vader is a terrifying symbol of the Empire's power. His total mastery of the dark side of the Force has made him a formidable foe, as many Rebel forces have discovered. But the Dark Lord of the Sith was not always an inhuman monster. He was once a man. A man called Skywalker...

Little is known about the early years of Anakin Skywalker. Pre-Imperial records show that he was an excellent pilot, and also incredibly gifted in the Force. The Jedi Knight Obi-Wan Kenobi recognised Anakin's power and decided to train him as a Jedi. But Kenobi lacked the experience of his teacher, Yoda, and failed to notice that Anakin Skywalker was being

seduced by the dark side.

When Obi-Wan realised what was happening to his student, Anakin was already strong with the dark side. The two fought a vicious lightsaber battle, during which Anakin fell into a molten pit. In the intense heat, all that had been Anakin Skywalker burned away and what rose from the pit had a

seething hatred for the Jedi Knights...and Obi-Wan Kenobi in particular. Darth Vader was born.

Because of his wounds, it is impossible for Vader to survive without a specially designed suit of armour. The sheer black durasteel helmet allows Vader to breathe, and also gives him enhanced vision and a synthesised voice. Vader's armour controls his temperature and protects his scarred body. Flowing cloaks conceal the hardware that keeps Vader alive.

But while Vader is rising to power working for the Empire, Obi-Wan Kenobi is keeping in touch with Anakin Skywalker's wife. Little did Vader know that his old life as Anakin Skywalker has given him two children. Children that Obi-Wan separates and hides from the Empire's view. Vader's children will be as strong in the Force as their father - and will be handy allies for the growing Rebellion. Vader's daughter, Leia, is adopted by the royal family of Alderaan. Vader's son, Luke, is raised by Obi-Wan's brother, Owen Lars, on the desert planet Tatooine. And so things remain, until one fateful day when a message in an R2 unit leads Luke Skywalker to an old man named Kenobi...and his destiny.

Darth Vaders Body Armour

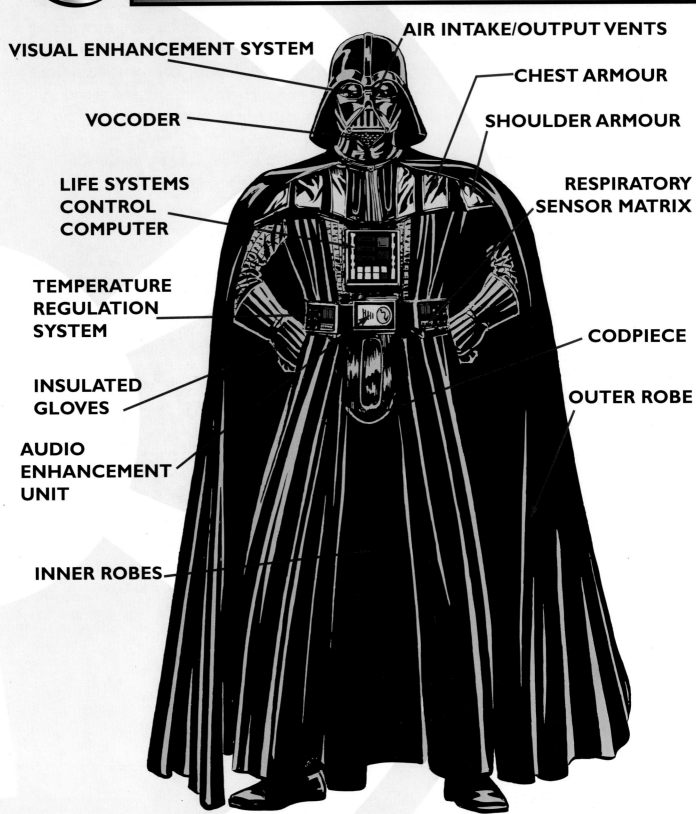

AIR INTAKE/OUTPUT VENTS

VISUAL ENHANCEMENT SYSTEM

CHEST ARMOUR

VOCODER

SHOULDER ARMOUR

LIFE SYSTEMS CONTROL COMPUTER

RESPIRATORY SENSOR MATRIX

TEMPERATURE REGULATION SYSTEM

CODPIECE

INSULATED GLOVES

OUTER ROBE

AUDIO ENHANCEMENT UNIT

INNER ROBES

Darth Vaders Face Mask

HEAD PROTECTION

VISUAL ENHANCEMENT SENSORS

ATMOSPHERE SENSORS

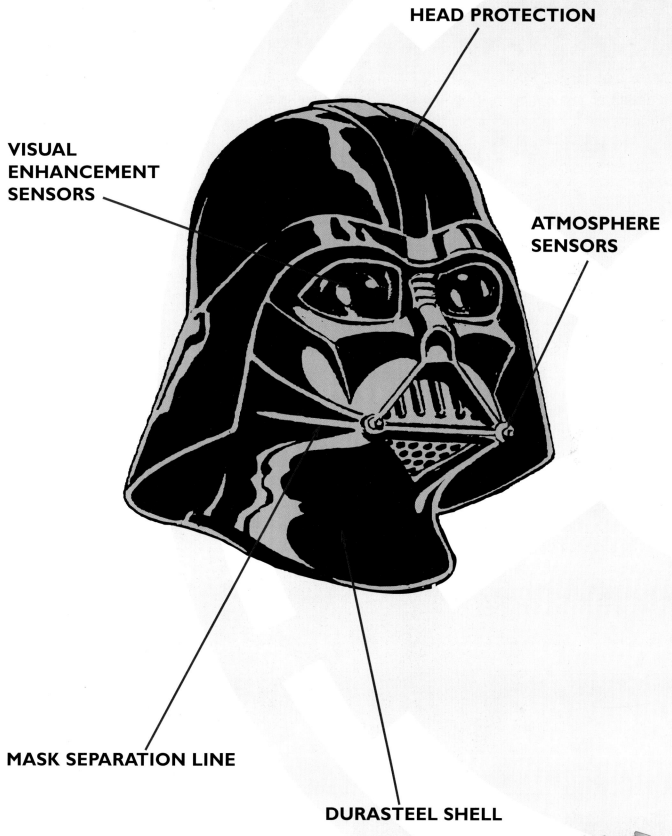

MASK SEPARATION LINE

DURASTEEL SHELL

Hoth Creature File

Wampa: a native of the ice planet Hoth, this savage creature roams the snow-covered landscape looking for prey. Often striking during blinding blizzards, those unfortunate enough to cross a wampa's path can expect to wake up hanging upside down in the monster's frozen cave, where they'll remain until the wampa gets hungry...

Tauntaun: a gentle, if ugly, beast of burden that is widely used for patrolling large areas quickly. A very useful creature on Hoth due to their adaptability to extremely cold temperatures, in the wild they live in caves and survive by eating the mosses and lichens that grow there. Their strange waddling run doesn't make them the most comfortable ride in the galaxy, but they get the job done. Providing, of course, that you can stand the smell!

Rebel Codebreaker

Attention, young Rebel! We have intercepted this transmission from an Imperial base somewhere in the galaxy. Each line of the message uses a different code. You must break the code so we can plan our next move.... Time is of the essence!

LINE 1:

URGENT. REQUEST STAR DESTROYERS IMMEDIATELY

LINE 2:

LEBER EASB DOCATEL REAN NAVIY MYSTES

LINE 3:

YEHT TSUM TON DNIF RUO TERCES ESAB

LINE 4:

LIRD VUDAR UND THA AMPARIR WELL URREVA
EN TWI DUYS FIR ENSPACTEIN

History Of The Empire

No record exists of how the Old Republic started. A peaceful and just galactic community, it was ruled by the wisdom of the Senate and protected by the ancient Jedi Knights for many hundred thousand years. The people of the galaxy slept well, convinced that the Republic was secure.

But dark forces were building within the Republic. After so many years of peace and prosperity, the Republic was not prepared for corruption from the inside. A charismatic,

ambitious senator named Palpatine had slowly but surely worked his way up through the political system. Outwardly he appeared genuine and decent, promising to sweep away the cobwebs from the Republic. But his motives were not as noble they first appeared, and there were some in the Senate who feared Palpatine and what he planned.

Eventually securing the position of president, Palpatine began to make huge changes. Those corrupt politicians who had helped him on his way were disposed of, and he proclaimed himself Emperor. With that, he began to dismantle the Old Republic and destroy the Jedi Knights. The peaceful ways of old were thrown aside, as massive warships were built and vast armies rose up to protect this evil new Empire. Gradually, spreading out from the core systems of the Old Republic, the tentacles of Imperial cruelty touched every planet in the galaxy.

Ruling by fear, and with a mysterious dark Jedi named Darth Vader by his side, the Emperor closed down the last remaining trace of the old ways - the Senate was no more.

The construction of the Death Star, a massive weapon capable of destroying an entire planet, was the final piece of Palpatine's evil plan. But those in the Senate who had seen Palpatine's motives all along were prepared. Just as his Empire grew, so did the Rebellion against him. Events had already been set in motion that would lead to the Emperor's defeat and downfall...

Stormtroopers

The backbone of the Imperial forces, stormtroopers are trained by the thousands by the Empire's Navy on the planet Caridia and then dispatched all over the galaxy to enforce Imperial obedience. Acting as soldiers, law enforcers, or security guards, their blank white helmets are recognised everywhere as a sign of Imperial might.

Stormtrooper training is designed to destroy any individual thoughts or motives. Stormtroopers have no names and are referred to only by number. Unquestioning loyalty to the Emperor is their entire existence.

All stormtroopers wear a black, two piece body glove which controls the trooper's temperature in extreme conditions. Over this they wear an armoured outer shell, made from eighteen plastisteel components that form a cocoon which supposedly protects the trooper from blaster fire. Past combat records show that this is far from the case.

The stormtrooper utility belt carries rations, batteries and a comlink. The helmet has its own air supply, and the black eye-lenses shield the trooper from glare and explosions. Variations in the armour design allow stormtroopers to operate in various conditions, including extreme cold, underwater, and the vacuum of space.

Stormtroopers Tech Spec

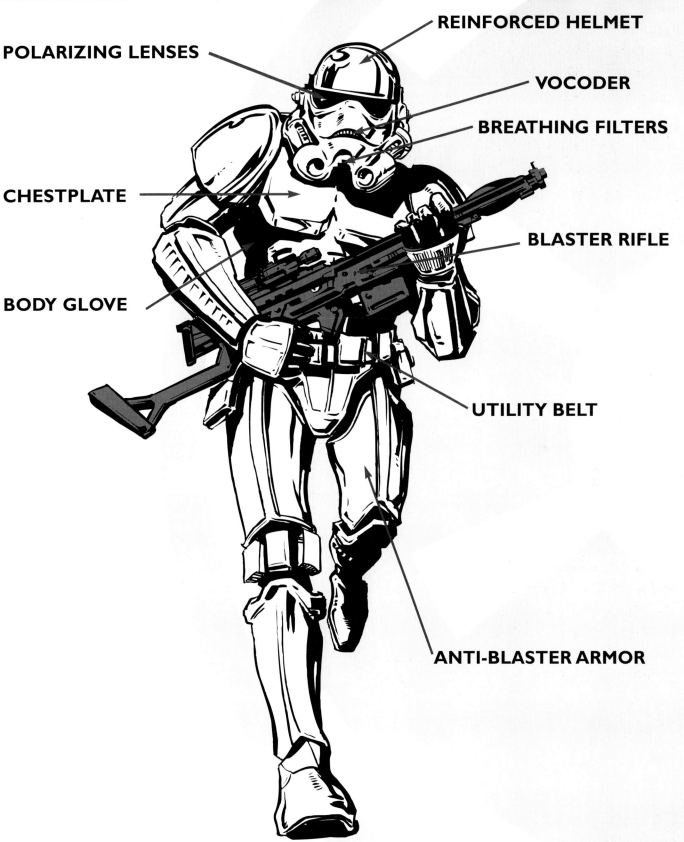

REINFORCED HELMET

POLARIZING LENSES

VOCODER

BREATHING FILTERS

CHESTPLATE

BLASTER RIFLE

BODY GLOVE

UTILITY BELT

ANTI-BLASTER ARMOR

Death Star Escape!

Luke, Han, and Chewie have gone to rescue Princess Leia. You are Obi-Wan Kenobi, and it's up to you to shut down the tractor beam so that everyone can escape. Can you reach the centre of the maze without running into stormtroopers or Darth Vader?

Tatooine Creature File

Sarlacc: Anchored in the dunes of Tatooine, the Sarlacc waits underground for victims to fall into its clutches. Of course, local gangsters like Jabba the Hutt sometimes give people a helping hand. Many hundred feet in length, the Sarlacc absorbs what little moisture the sand holds through its root limbs, while its body is a huge armoured mass in which food is slowly digested over thousands of years.

Bantha: Native to Tatooine, these creatures are the chosen transport of the vicious Tusken Raiders. Standing between two and three metres tall, the bantha has a unique relationship with the Sand People. They are treated as almost equal members of Tusken tribes and have a unique telepathic bond with their rider. Sand People ride banthas in single file, to hide their numbers.

39

C-3PO

A translator and protocol droid fluent in over six million languages, C-3PO has, like all other human/cyborg relations units, been programmed to mimic human behaviour and speech as closely as possible. Originally a shiny gold colour, his many adventures have left him with several silver-plated limbs, where damage has made replacement necessary.

C-3PO and his companion R2-D2 have both had several masters over the years. Having led eventful lives, the two droids have, for one reason or another, avoided the frequent memory wipes that regulate personality development in droids.

As a result, several personality traits have developed and become a part of C-3PO's character, such as a strong sense of loyalty and extremely high intelligence.

On the other hand, C-3PO has a fear of space travel, not a very good quality for a droid that travels all over the galaxy. Much to the amusement of the other Rebels, he has also become something of a worrier. But despite his fussy nature, C-3PO has played an important role in the downfall of the Empire.

C-3PO Tech Spec

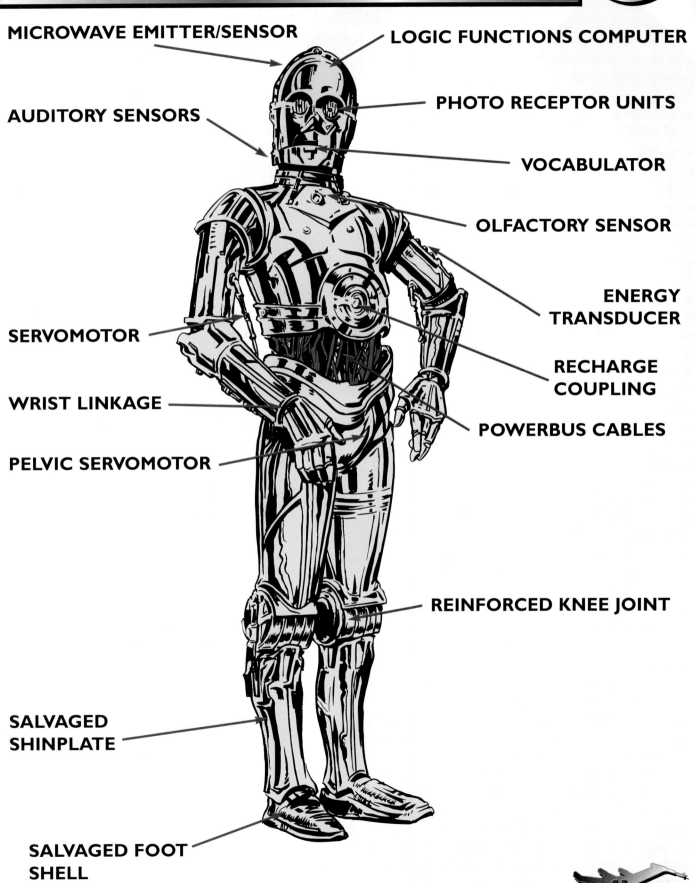

MICROWAVE EMITTER/SENSOR

LOGIC FUNCTIONS COMPUTER

AUDITORY SENSORS

PHOTO RECEPTOR UNITS

VOCABULATOR

OLFACTORY SENSOR

ENERGY TRANSDUCER

SERVOMOTOR

RECHARGE COUPLING

WRIST LINKAGE

POWERBUS CABLES

PELVIC SERVOMOTOR

REINFORCED KNEE JOINT

SALVAGED SHINPLATE

SALVAGED FOOT SHELL

Of all the astromech droids in the service of the Rebellion, it is a humble tripodal R2 utility unit that holds the key to destroying the first Death Star. R2-D2 is the droid Leia uses to deliver the Death Star plans to Obi-Wan Kenobi.

Like all astromech droids, R2 has many functions. His primary function is interfacing with fighter craft, such as the X-wing, as well as monitoring flight performance, navigation, and repairs. His speech is restricted to beeps and whistles, but when docked with a fighter, his words are translated by a computer screen for the pilot.

His counterpart droid C-3PO often translates for R2 and even a few humans are able to translate his speech.

Two legs with caterpillar treads provide support, and a third leg can be extended for mobility.
Other facilities include a computer link, fire extinguisher, electric shock prod, spotlight, grabbing claw, laser welder, and a circular saw.

R2-D2 Tech Spec

ACCESS PANEL

RADAR EYE

INFRARED RECEPTOR

FUNCTION INDICATORS

HARD DATA INPUT

PACECRAFT INKAGE ND REPAIR ARMS

LOUDSPEAKER

SYSTEM VENTILATION

RECHARGE COUPLING

HOLOGRAPHIC PROJECTOR

SENSORY INPUT HEAD

UTILITY FUNCTIONS DOOR (BOTH SIDES)

ACTUATING COUPLER

BTU EXHAUST WAVE

POWER CELLS

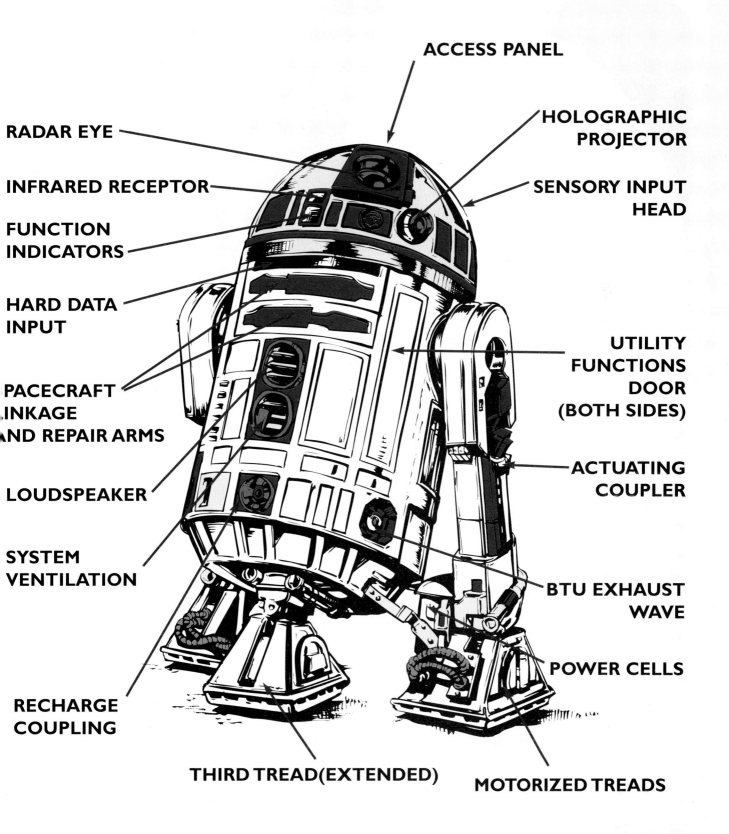

THIRD TREAD(EXTENDED)

MOTORIZED TREADS

43

Can You Resist The Dark Side?

Darth Vader has ruled the galaxy using his powerful Jedi mind powers. Here's a way to see his dark strength in action. Stare at the picture below, concentrating on the spot in the middle of Darth Vader's helmet. Don't blink yet! Keep staring for 30 seconds, and then quickly look at a blank wall. Now blink, and the Dark Lord of the Sith will appear before your eyes!

Power Of The Jedi
(from the records of the Yavin 4 Jedi Academy)

The Jedi Knights draw their power from the Force - a mysterious energy field that links all living things. In the words of Obi-Wan Kenobi, "it surrounds us and penetrates us. It binds the galaxy together."

Those who are in tune with the Force, and trained to control and understand it, form the

core of the Jedi Knights. However, the Force is neither good nor evil. It is both at the same time, with a light side and a dark side. The temptation to give in to the dark side is strong, which is why only Jedi Masters such as Yoda are allowed to train young Jedi. Obi-Wan Kenobi starts to teach Anakin Skywalker, but is unable to prevent Skywalker's slide into evil.

Once the Force is mastered, it becomes a powerful ally. A Jedi is able to use the Force to manipulate the world around him. Objects can be levitated and moved from a distance, blaster bolts can be deflected, and the minds of weaker beings can be clouded and controlled. But the Jedi only ever uses their power for defence, never to attack.

Weapon Of The Jedi

Before the rise of the Empire, the Old Republic was kept at peace by the noble and peaceful Jedi Knights. With the Force as their guide, the Jedi created calm confidence in the citizens they protected.

The chosen weapon of the Jedi is the lightsaber. Based on ancient technology, this graceful blade of light requires great skill to master and it is traditional for a Jedi to build their own lightsabers. A power cell is placed in the handgrip, and a focussing core channels the energy through crystallite lenses to create a humming "blade" of pure light.

All lightsabers are based on these same core elements, although differences in design account for the variation in the colour of lightsaber blades.

As Obi-Wan Kenobi told young Luke Skywalker, the lightsaber wasn't "clumsy or random" like a blaster. It was "an elegant weapon for a more civilised time."

A true Jedi can use the lightsaber, along with the Force, to diffuse dangerous situations.

Lightsabers Tech Spec

POWER CELL

LENS ASSEMBLY

HANDGRIP

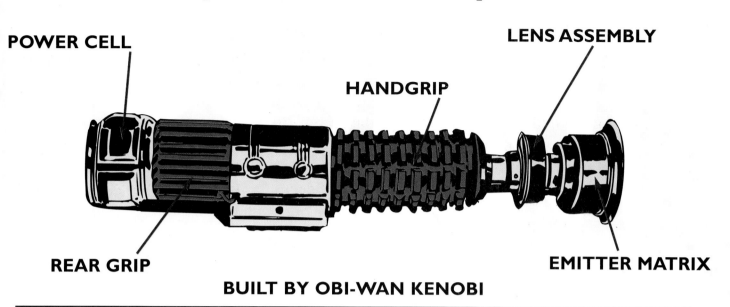

REAR GRIP

EMITTER MATRIX

BUILT BY OBI-WAN KENOBI

BELT RING

POWER CELL/HANDGRIP

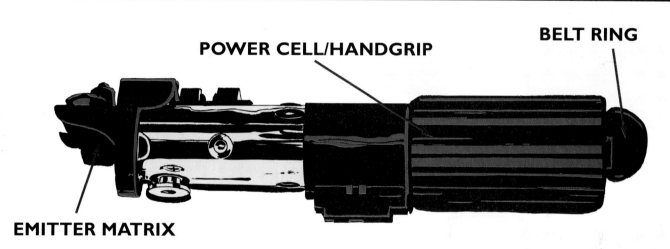

EMITTER MATRIX

BUILT BY ANAKIN SKYWALKER

POWER CELL

HANDGRIP

LENS ASSEMBLY

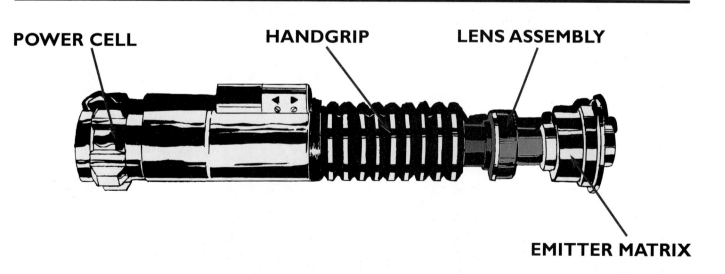

EMITTER MATRIX

BUILT BY LUKE SKYWALKER

Weapons Of The Empire

The standard weapon of the Imperial forces, and indeed most civilians, the blaster is a reliable and easy to use weapon ideal for attack and defence. Regardless of whether it's a handheld pistol or a ship-mounted turret, blaster technology is essentially the same. Using laser beams, blasters fire pulses of focussed light combined with accelerated high-energy particles. By adjusting the power output, the blaster can be set to stun, or can vapourise anything short of reinforced durasteel.

Three companies produce blaster weaponry, Merr-Sonn Munitions, SoroSuub Corporation, and BlasTech Industries. Merr-Sonn and SoroSuub both produce weapons exclusively for the Empire, but their blasters still find their way onto the black market. Standard issue for stormtroopers is the blaster rifle, a more powerful weapon with longer range.

Luke, in a stormtrooper uniform, holding a blaster rifle

Han Solo with a blaster pistol

48

Blaster Tech Spec

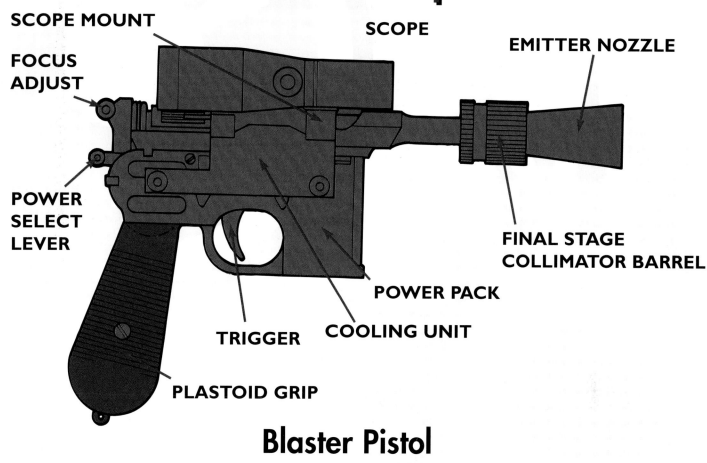

SCOPE MOUNT

FOCUS ADJUST

POWER SELECT LEVER

SCOPE

EMITTER NOZZLE

FINAL STAGE COLLIMATOR BARREL

POWER PACK

COOLING UNIT

TRIGGER

PLASTOID GRIP

Blaster Pistol

Blaster Rifle

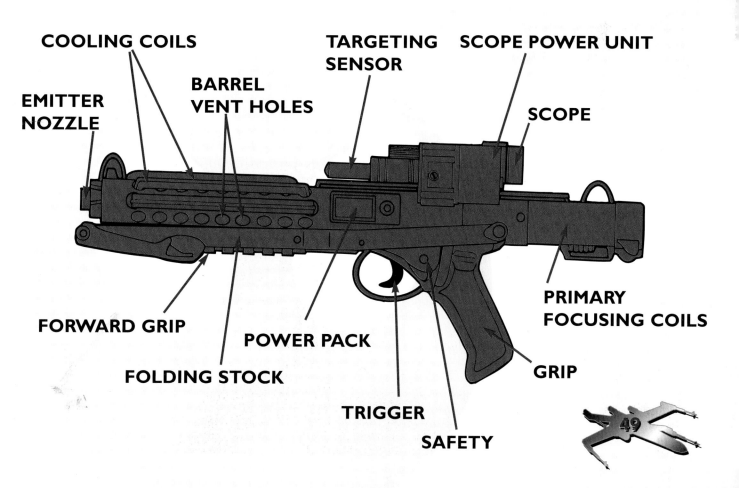

COOLING COILS

BARREL VENT HOLES

TARGETING SENSOR

SCOPE POWER UNIT

SCOPE

EMITTER NOZZLE

FORWARD GRIP

FOLDING STOCK

POWER PACK

TRIGGER

SAFETY

GRIP

PRIMARY FOCUSING COILS

49

The Way Of The Jedi

Despite his tiny size and bumbling manner, Yoda is the greatest of the Jedi Masters. The teacher of Obi-Wan Kenobi, he also tutored Luke Skywalker in the ways of the Force. His words of wisdom are included here, in the hope of inspiring a new generation of Jedi.

A great warrior. Wars not make one great.

Adventure. Excitement. A Jedi craves not these things.

Only different in your mind. You must unlearn what you have learned.

Try not. Do or do not. There is no try.

My ally is the Force. And a powerful ally it is. Life creates it, makes it grow.
Its energy surrounds and binds us.

Luminous beings are we... not this crude matter.

Anger... Fear... Aggression the dark side of the Force are they. Easily they flow,
quick to join you in a fight. If once you start down the dark path.
Forever will it dominate your destiny.

Size matters not. Judge me by my size do you?

Through the Force, things you will see.

When 900 years old you reach, look as good you will not.

When gone I am, the last of the Jedi will you be.

51

Rebel Pilot Tech Spec

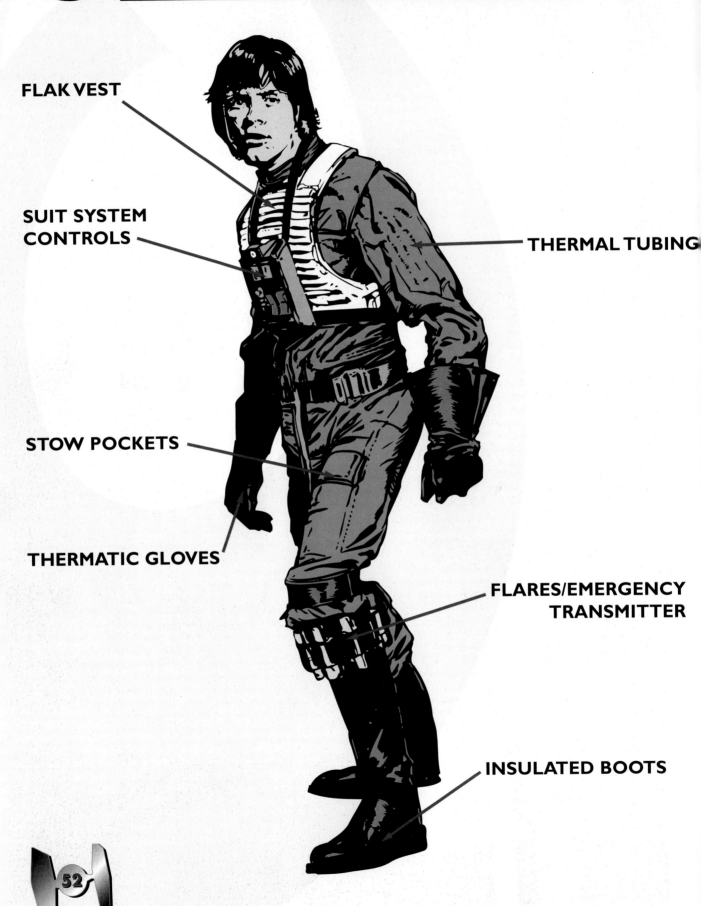

FLAK VEST

SUIT SYSTEM CONTROLS

THERMAL TUBING

STOW POCKETS

THERMATIC GLOVES

FLARES/EMERGENCY TRANSMITTER

INSULATED BOOTS

Asteroid Escape

Han, Chewie, Leia, and C-3PO have blasted away from Hoth with the Empire hot on their heels. In front of them is an asteroid field, and behind them are hoardes of TIE fighters! Guide them through the asteroids to safety.

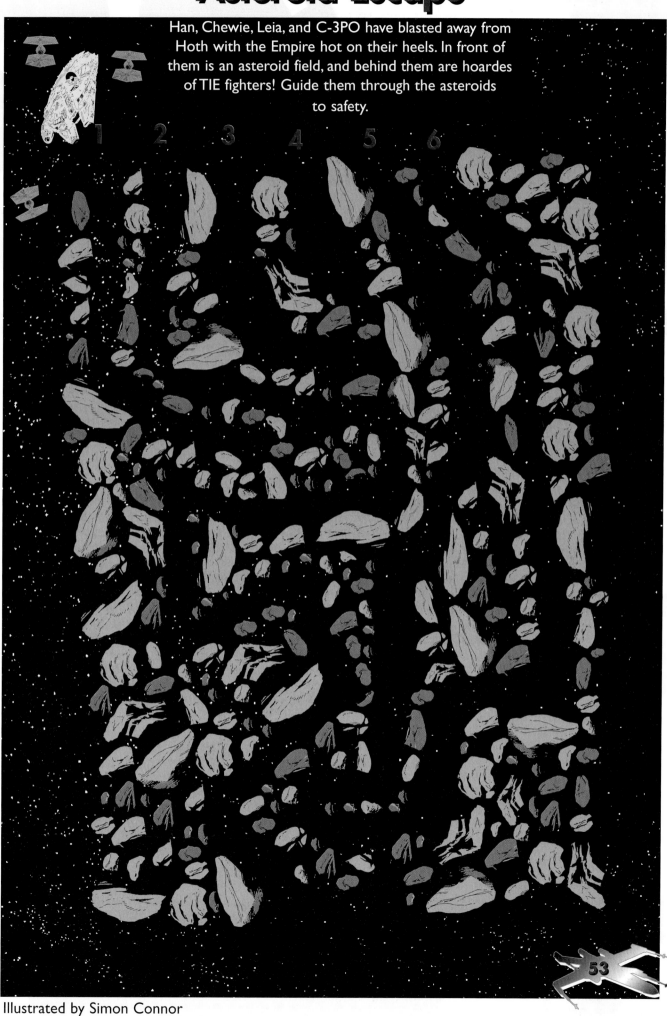

1   2   3   4   5   6

53

Illustrated by Simon Connor

How Much Do You Know About Darth Vader?

The Dark Lord of the Sith is shrouded in mystery, but do you know enough about the Empire's terrifying dark leader to pass this test?

1. Who was the Dark Lord of the Sith before he became Darth Vader?
Obi-Wan Kenobi
Anakin Skywalker
Lando Calrissian

2. Where does Luke Skywalker see Darth Vader for the first time?
The Death Star
Mos Eisley Spaceport
Jabba's Palace

3. Who are Darth Vader's two children?
R2-D2 and C-3P0
Luke and Leia
Han Solo and Chewbacca

4. What does Anakin Skywalker train as before turning to the dark side of the Force?
A Galactic Guardian
A Champion of Justice
A Jedi Knight

5. What colour is Darth Vader's lightsaber?
Blue
Green
Red

6. Which bounty hunter tracked down the *Millennium Falcon* for Darth Vader?
Boba Fett
Greedo
Bib Fortuna

7. What is the name of the deadly battle station where Darth Vader and Obi-Wan Kenobi fight to the death?
Star Destroyer
TIE fighter
Death Star

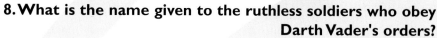

8. What is the name given to the ruthless soldiers who obey Darth Vader's orders?
Stormtroopers
Ewoks
Gamorrean Guards

9. What is the name of Darth Vader's master?
Admiral Ackbar
Emperor Palpatine
Jabba the Hutt

10. Darth Vader wears a distinctive type of clothing. What is it?
Desert wrap and dust mask
A black robe, helmet, and body armour
Wookiee suit and crossbow

11. In which of the three films does Darth Vader take his mask off?
Star Wars
The Empire Strikes Back
Return of the Jedi

12. Which part of Vader's body does Luke cut off on the second Death Star?
Right Ear
Left Hand
Right Hand

13. Darth Vader was nicknamed the 'Dark Lord of the Sith'. The Sith was;
A mysterious group with strong powers
The closest planet to the Death Star
Vader's spaceship

14. How does Vader kill the Emperor?
Throws him out of an airlock into space
Throws him into the reactor of the second Death Star
Strangles him

15. Who tries to train Anakin Skywalker as a Jedi, and fails?
Yoda
Luke Skywalker
Obi-Wan Kenobi

Planet File: Hoth

Hoth is not only the name of a star system, it is also the name of the sixth planet in that star system. Far from any civilised worlds, it is this frozen planet that the Rebels choose as their main base after the destruction of the first Death Star.

Hoth is bitterly cold, although it is possible for humans to tolerate the cold during the day, if wearing thermal clothing. At night, though, the temperature plummets and to remain outside when darkness falls on Hoth is suicidal.

Although conditions are harsh, some lifeforms do exist on Hoth. The tauntaun is a placid creature, a fact that the Rebels use to their advantage when they tame tauntauns for use as mounts for scout patrols. Also native to Hoth is the wampa. A ferocious predator, wampas strike suddenly, their white fur hiding them in the snow. They drag their unconcious prey back to their caves and hang them upside down until they are ready to feed.

The Rebels equipment and vehicles have to be specially adapted for this extreme cold, which is just as well. The Empire finds the Rebel base after sending out thousands of probe droids across the galaxy, and attacks with AT-AT walkers. The Rebel base is destroyed in the following battle, although the Rebels themselves escape. The base was later used by the Empire to house troops and hold prisoners.

Night Falls On Hoth

Luke Skywalker has escaped from the wampa, but now must face the freezing Hoth night alone. As he collapses into the swirling snow, he sees a vision from the corner of his eye...Obi-Wan Kenobi? But Luke is tired and cold. Which of these visions is the real Obi-Wan? Only one of them is different. Can you spot it?

How Much Do You Know About Han Solo?

Little is known about Han Solo's past, and that's the way he likes it. Yet despite his lawless history, the quick witted rogue becomes one of the greatest heroes of the Rebellion. See how much you remember about his adventures.

1. Where does Luke Skywalker first meet Han?
On the Death Star
The Mos Eisley Cantina
At Han's house

2. Chewbacca is Han's copilot and friend. But what species is he?
Wookiee
Ewok
Bantha

3. When Han leads the scout team on the Forest Moon of Endor, what is his rank?
Cadet
Admiral
General

4. What is the name of the substance Han is frozen in on Cloud City?
Plastisteel
Carbonite
Space Clay

5. What is the name of the bounty hunter who captures Han?
Boba Fett
IG-88
Dengar

6. When Han is freed from his frozen prison, what is wrong with him?
He has become a robot
He is blind
He has turned green

7. To whom does Han owe money?
Boba Fett
Obi-Wan Kenobi
Jabba the Hutt

8. Who owns the *Millennium Falcon* before Han?
Chewbacca
Lando Calrissian
Admiral Ackbar

9. How does Han save Luke from freezing to death on Hoth?

He gives him his coat

He lights a big fire

He puts Luke inside his tauntaun's body

10. When Han, Leia, Chewie, and C-3PO hide from the Empire inside an asteroid, what goes wrong?

The asteroid crashes onto a planet

They are actually inside a giant space slug

The asteroid is a secret Imperial base

11. Who does Han save from falling into the Sarlaac's mouth?

Chewbacca

Luke Skywalker

Lando Calrissian

12. In the Mos Eisley Cantina, Han has a close encounter with Greedo, one of Jabba's henchmen. What happens?

Greedo forgives Han and lets him go

Han shoots Greedo under the table

Han pays Greedo the money he owes and leaves

13. Which planet does Han Solo come from?

Corellia

Alderaan

Tatooine

14. What do Han and Chewie do before they become involved in the Rebellion?

Serve as soldiers

Work as mechanics

Smuggle illegal cargo

15. How does Han help Luke destroy the first Death Star?

He shows Luke where to fire his torpedoes

He blasts the TIE fighters on Luke's tail

He teaches Luke how to fly

Millennium Falcon

Han Solo calls it "the fastest hunk of junk in the galaxy", and the *Millennium Falcon* lives up to his boasts time after time. Once upon a time the *Falcon* was a standard Corellian stock light freighter, but Han has made many modifications to turn the battered freighter into a smugglers dream.

Underneath the ramshackle appearance is a powerful hyperdrive, twice as fast as any Imperial warship, and a complex sensor array that allows Han and his Wookiee copilot Chewbacca to detect trouble before it arrives. Secret compartments are used to hide smuggled cargo, and sometimes even the crew themselves! Despite all its technology, the *Falcon* is not the most reliable ship, and last minute repairs are common before making the jump to lightspeed.

The *Millennium Falcon* has not always been Han's ship. Han won it from Lando Calrissian in a game of sabacc, and Lando himself had won it early in his gambling career. Later, when the time comes to attack the second Death Star, Lando takes the helm of the *Falcon* once again, while Han leads the scout team on Endor. With the Empire crushed, Han Solo and his beloved *Falcon* are reunited.

Answers

Page 20
How Much Do You Know About Luke Skywalker?

1. Tatooine, 2. They run a moisture farm, 3. Wampa, 4. Darth Vader, 5. He fires torpedoes into an exhaust port, 6. A stormtrooper, 7. Right, 8. Twice, 9. In a stolen shuttle, 10. Yoda, 11. He crushes it under a giant door, 12. Uncle Owen and Aunt Beru, 13. He nearly got into a fight,
14. On speederbikes, 15. Blue

Page 23: Use The Force

Han Solo, Chewbacca, Princess Leia, Ben Kenobi

Page 24
How Much Do You Know About The Droids?

1. Six million, 2. The plans for the Death Star, 3. Serves drinks, 4. Translates, 5. He gets blown to pieces, 6. Tatooine, 7. Jawas, 8. He falls in the swamp, 9. He uses a miniature saw to cut the net, 10. He tosses a lightsaber for Luke to catch, 11. R2-D2, 12. Master Luke, 13. Luke's uncle buys an R5 robot instead of R2-D2, but it blows its motivator, 14. Golden Rod, 15. They have to wait outside

Page 27
Wordsearch

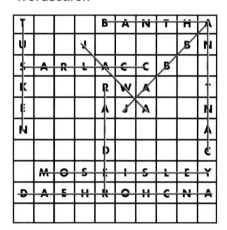

Page 33: Rebel Codebreaker

LINE 1: Hold the message to a mirror
LINE 2: Swap the first and last letters of each word
LINE 3: Each word is written backwards
LINE 4: A = E, E = I, I = O, O = U, U = A

Page 54
How Much Do You Know About Darth Vader?

1. Anakin Skywalker, 2. The Death Star, 3. Luke and Leia, 4. A Jedi Knight, 5. Red, 6. Boba Fett, 7. Death Star, 8. Stormtroopers, 9. Emperor Palpatine, 10. Black robe, helmet and body armour, 11. Return of the Jedi, 12. Right hand, 13. A mysterious group with strong powers, 14. Throws him into the reactor of the second Death Star, 15. Obi Wan Kenobi

Page 58
How Much Do You Know About Han Solo?

1. The Mos Eisley Cantina, 2. Wookiee, 3. General, 4. Carbonite, 5. Boba Fett, 6. He is blind, 7. Jabba the Hutt, 8. Lando Calrissian, 9. He puts Luke inside his tauntaun, 10. They are actually inside a giant space slug, 11. Lando Calrissian, 12. Han shoots Greedo under the table, 13. Corellia,
14. Smuggle illegal cargo, 15. He blasts the TIE fighters on Luke's tail